– For Abby, Asher & Jonah – you bring daily joy and inspiration!

Written & Illustrated by Chris Workman

A FEW NOTES OF ACKNOWLEDGEMENT AND APPRECIATION

Thanks to the 100+ supporters who believed in this project and contributed to the book's Indiegogo campaign, and to the media who helped spread the word during this introductory period. Without your help this project would have never been possible!

Special thanks to Tom Moore, Craig Van Eaton, Brian Barr, Jade Gurss, Ryan Gray, Eve Hewitt and John Hindbaugh for your support and guidance through this process.

To my dad and brother for taking me to my first race and igniting my life-long love of racing, and to my mom for her endless encouragement to chase this dream, And to my wife, Rachel, for being my rock through the highs and lows of this wonderful journey!

This project has been fortunate to receive support from many notable participants in the 24 Hours of Le Mans in 1956. The trade marks "JAGUAR", "D-TYPE", "C-TYPE", "XK" and "XK120" are registered trade marks of Jaguar Land Rover Limited. The JAGUAR trade marks have been reproduced in this book with the express permission of Jaguar Land Rover Limited. Special thanks to Jaguar Heritage for providing research images. The 24 Hours of Le Mans is a registered trademark of the Automobile Club de l'Ouest and used with permission. The names and likeness of Aston Martin, the Aston Martin DB3S, Ecurie Ecosse race team and Sir Stirling Moss are used with permission.

For inquiries regarding distribution and sales please contact Chris Workman at cworkman@apexlegends.com. Apex Legends is a division of Apex Communications Group, LLC.

First printing May 2015.

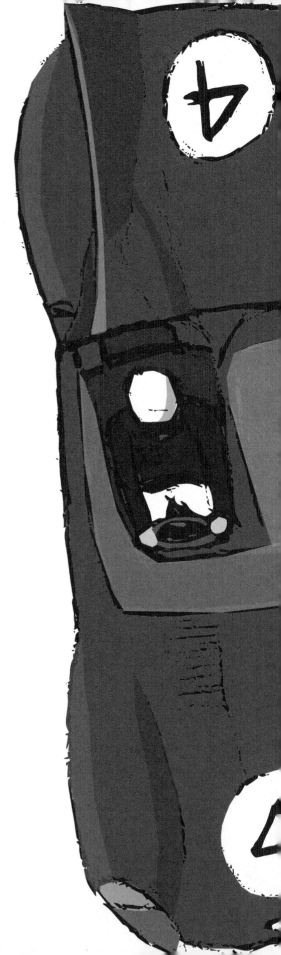

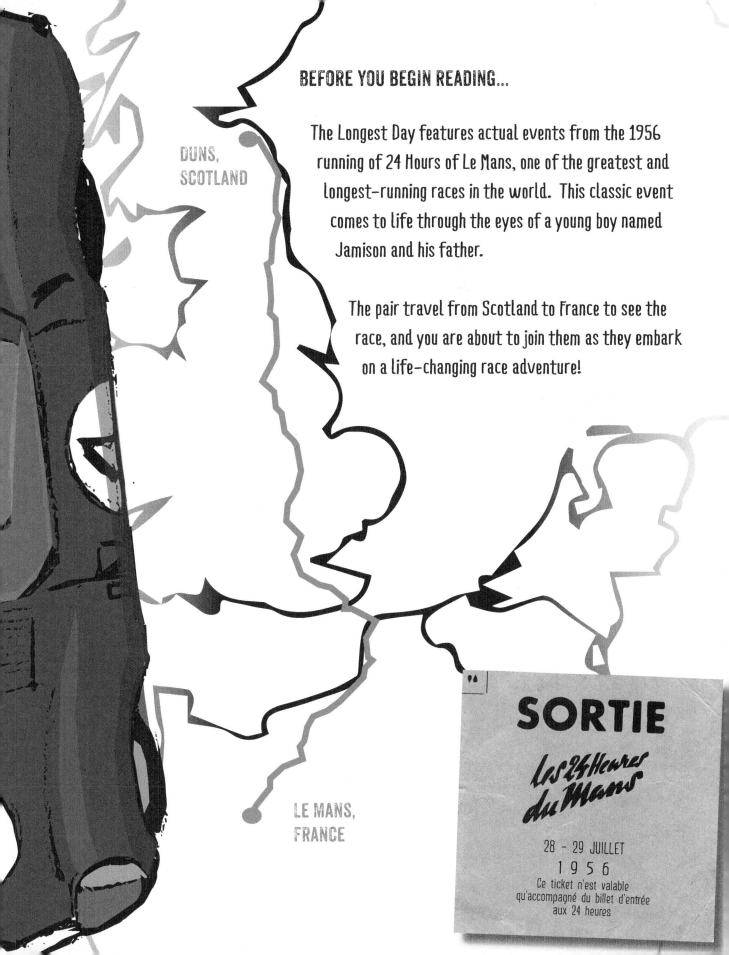

BEFORE YOU BEGIN READING...

The Longest Day features actual events from the 1956 running of 24 Hours of Le Mans, one of the greatest and longest-running races in the world. This classic event comes to life through the eyes of a young boy named Jamison and his father.

The pair travel from Scotland to France to see the race, and you are about to join them as they embark on a life-changing race adventure!

DUNS,
SCOTLAND

LE MANS,
FRANCE

SORTIE

Les 24 Heures du Mans

28 - 29 JUILLET
1 9 5 6
Ce ticket n'est valable
qu'accompagné du billet d'entrée
aux 24 heures

IF YOU HAVE NEVER BEEN TO LE MANS...

The Longest Day provides an authentic representation of what it would have been like to experience the 24 Hours of Le Mans during a classic era featuring truly beautiful cars and fantastic drivers. If you aren't familiar with Le Mans or endurance racing these quick reference terms will be useful. These terms are just as relevant if you watch or attend a modern-day endurance race!

CO-DRIVER

In the 1950's each racecar had two drivers; these drivers would switch places throughout the 24 hour race period so they could rest. Today due to safety and fatigue concerns each car has a minimum of three drivers.

ECURIE ECOSSE

While this may look like a mouthful to say, Ecurie Ecosse is French for "Team Scotland". The Ecurie Ecosse team competed in sports car racing and some grand prix events from the 1950's – 1960's. The team name has been revived several times; today the team is a strong competitor in European sports car racing events.

GARAGE

For decades many of the teams set up temporary garages in the village of Le Mans to work on their racecars. This was due to a shortage of garage space at the track, however today all race teams have garage space at the Le Mans circuit.

LE MANS START

From the first Le Mans race in 1923 until 1969, the race started with the drivers lining up across the track from their cars. At the drop of the green flag they ran across the track, jumped into their cars, started them, and then raced away. While an entertaining spectacle, this tradition was (not surprisingly) dropped in the name of safety.

MULTIPLE CLASSES OF CARS

Le Mans-style endurance racing features multiple types of cars, or "classes", racing at the same time. All the cars compete to be the overall winner, however trophies are also awarded based on finishing position within each class. In 1956 engine size was used to define the race classes, however today they are based on a number of factors including weight, engine power and other performance elements.

SCRUTINEERING

This celebratory event is held in the Village of Le Mans several days before the race. Officials inspect each car to make sure they are safe and built to the rules for the race. Scrutineering is exciting for fans because they are able to get close to the cars and often meet the drivers.

WORKS TEAM

This term is used to describe a race team that is either owned or funded by a car manufacturer. Aston Martin, Jaguar, Porsche and other companies operated race teams featured in this book. Today many manufacturers continue to develop and race cars to showcase their engineering capabilities for the world to see at Le Mans!

AND NOW THE JOURNEY BEGINS!

EVERYONE in Jamison's home town in Scotland has been excited because a local boy named Jim Clark had just won his first car race. Jamison asked his father if he could see a race, so his father is taking him on the ferry from England to France to see the greatest car race in the world, THE 24 HOURS OF LE MANS!

While on the ferry, Jamison's father tells stories about when he raced at Le Mans before Jamison was born.

Even though he never won the race, **HIS FATHER LOVED LE MANS** and he couldn't wait to take Jamison there.

His father called the 24 Hours of Le Mans **"THE LONGEST DAY"** because it was so long and grueling!

Jamison and his father arrive in the historic village of Le Mans the day before the race just in time for an event called SCRUTINEERING.

A festive atmosphere greets them as a crowd of fans and race officials inspect all the amazing, colorful cars.

While looking at a sleek silver Porsche they see David, a friend of Jamison's father. David manages the Scottish ECURIE ECOSSE team and he invites the boy and his father to visit the team's garage to get a close look at their JAGUAR D-TYPE racecar!

When they get to the garage Jamison gets an up-close look at the
BEAUTIFUL DARK BLUE JAGUAR.

David talks to Jamison's father about the race. His team will be competing against the best "Works" teams from England, France, Germany and Italy in a **RACE OF BOTH SPEED AND SURVIVAL.** It will be difficult for a small team like David's to win Le Mans!

As they say goodbye, David tells Jamison and his father that they are welcome to **VISIT THE TEAM'S PITS** before the race.

As father and son walk to the pits, they buy a race program so Jamison can study the lengthy track layout.

Jamison can't wait to see the cars speed down the **3 MILE LONG** Mulsanne straight!

The race team crews are busy in the pits **TINKERING WITH THE RACECARS**, adding fuel and checking tires and brakes.

24 HEURES DU MANS

Tetre Rouge

Esses

Dunlop Curve

Jamison is **EXCITED FOR RACE DAY!** When he and his father arrive at the track they see huge grandstands and a **FERRIS WHEEL.** He hears the rumbling noise of engines as pit crews get the cars ready for The Longest Day.

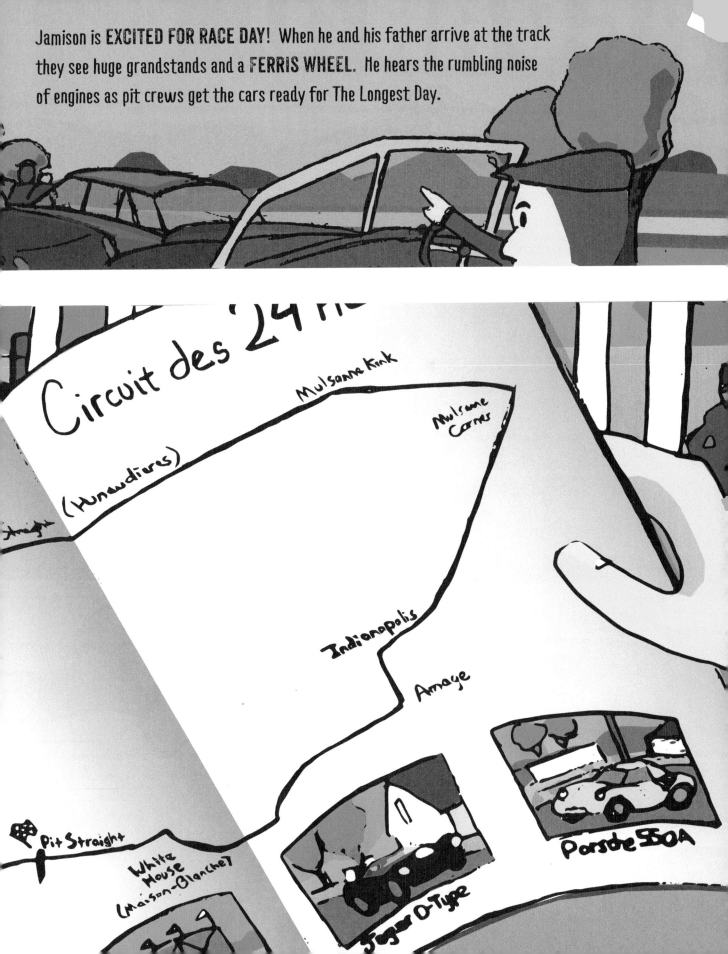

It begins drizzling right before the start of the race. The crowd anxiously watches the DRIVERS LINE UP across the track from their racecars.

STANGUELLINI ⑤⑤   STANGUELLINI ⑤③   LAROIL

THE GREEN FLAG DROPS   and the drivers run across the track.

Jamison sees Ron jump into his Jaguar...

AND FIRE UP THE ENGINE!

Stirling Moss sprints across the track and gets to his car first. HE STORMS OFF into the lead in his green Aston Martin DB3S. The noise from the cheering crowd and the VRROOOOOOOOMMMMMMM of the racecar engines is very loud!

THE LONGEST DAY HAS BEGUN!

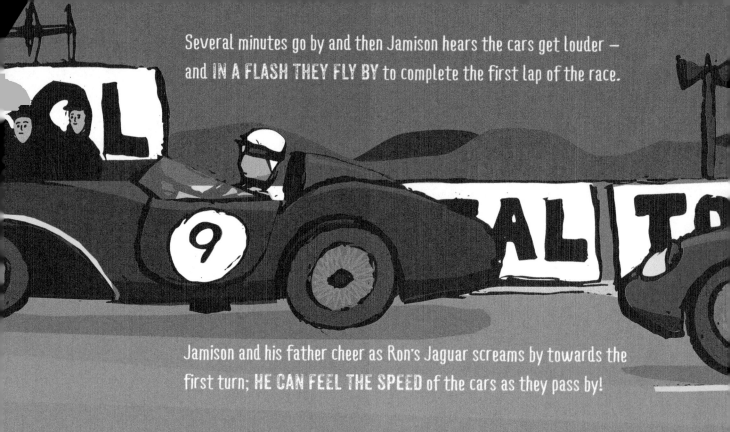

Several minutes go by and then Jamison hears the cars get louder — and **IN A FLASH THEY FLY BY** to complete the first lap of the race.

Jamison and his father cheer as Ron's Jaguar screams by towards the first turn; **HE CAN FEEL THE SPEED** of the cars as they pass by!

A few laps later, **THE ECURIE ECOSSE TEAM GETS A LUCKY BREAK.** The announcer tells the crowd that the driver of the second place Jaguar has spun on the wet track and hit the wall, causing damage to his car.

Then the drivers in the next two cars collide –
JUST LIKE THAT RON HAS MOVED UP TO FOURTH PLACE!

After the cars make their first pit stops
for gas, Jamison and his father leave their
grandstand seats to EXPLORE
other parts of the track.

MOTUL   LUCAS

32

As they walk across one of the Dunlop Bridges Jamison can actually see Ron's dark blue Jaguar **FLASH BY** through cracks in the wood planks beneath his feet.

Jamison watches all the different types of racecars **AT TOP SPEED** while walking along the Mulsanne straightaway. He decides to pick a favorite to win the class for smaller-engine cars.

After a few minutes Jamison picks a silver Porsche 550 Le Mans Coupe that **SHOOTS BY THEM LIKE A SPEEDING BULLET!**

Jamison is thirsty so they stop to get a drink at a trackside café. He asks his father why the café, as well as houses and other buildings, were so close to the track. His father explains that the track is used as a public road all year long, except for this **ONE MAGICAL WEEKEND** when The Longest Day occurs.

As the boy daydreams about driving on the race track his father **ERUPTS INTO A ROARING CHEER.** Jamison turns just in time to see Ron's Jaguar passing Stirling's Aston Martin. He jumps up and down with excitement!

Seven hours into the race the top three cars are still racing close together. Earlier Ron and Stirling both **SWITCHED PLACES** with their co-drivers to rest. Now the Ecurie Ecosse Jaguar is in second place behind the leading Aston Martin.

Jamison convinces his father to take another two turns on the Ferris wheel so they can keep **WATCHING THE TIGHT BATTLE** on track from up high!

Exhausted from the fun day, Jamison and his father set up their tent to get some rest. As he lies in his sleeping bag next to his father and begins drifting off to sleep, Jamison smiles as he hears the roaring symphony of 4, 6, 8 and 12 cylinder engines echo in the cool evening air.

IT WAS AT THAT POINT HE FELL IN LOVE WITH RACING.

Jamison and his father wake up to get some breakfast. They are both anxious to get an update on the overnight race action and listen closely to the PA announcer.

Then they hear an exciting piece of news – Ron is back in the car and **CLOSING IN ON STIRLING** for the lead!

Jamison and his father hear more updates once they return to their grandstand seats.

Overnight, an Italian car and a Porsche collided and **CRASHED HEAVILY.** And, one of the Aston Martin Works cars slid on the wet track and had a very bad accident. **THANKFULLY EVERYONE IS OK.**

Many cars retired from the race with **MECHANICAL PROBLEMS.**

It is down to Ron and Stirling for a fight to the finish! With so many cars out of the race winning isn't just about who's car is quickest; **IT'S ABOUT SURVIVAL.**

Jamison sees Ron tuck to the inside of the Aston Martin as the two cars scream up the pit straight. The Jaguar is **PERFECTLY POSITIONED** and makes the pass into the first turn.

Jamison screams and grabs his father's arm. **HE CAN'T BELIEVE IT!**

The drivers continue their duel over the next few laps. Stirling is ready to strike – one tiny mistake from Ron and he will be in the lead again. Suddenly Jamison sees Stirling's Aston Martin **LIMP INTO THE PITS.**

The mechanics look under the rear of the car. "GEARBOX PROBLEMS," Jamison's father says. Jamison lets out a SIGH OF RELIEF.

Ecurie Ecosse will win The Longest Day... IF THEIR CAR DOESN'T BREAK DOWN. Even so, Jamison is sad to see the epic battle is over; he smiles when Stirling slowly exits the pits to defend second place.

As The Longest Day comes to a close, Jamison and his Father **SOAK IN THE MOMENT.** A tiny Scottish team is about to beat the world's best teams to win the 24 Hours of Le Mans.

The sound of bagpipes come through the PA system as the **ECURIE ECOSSE JAGUAR** TAKES **THE CHECKERED FLAG!**

Jamison and his father make their way to celebrate with the team. Ron pulls his weathered Jaguar into **VICTORY LANE** and climbs out. He embraces David and his co-driver and waves to the crowd. Then, out of the corner of his eyes he sees Jamison and his father cheering.

Ron gives Jamison a thumbs up and tosses him his race goggles as he steps to the top of the podium to receive the race trophy. Jamison catches the goggles and **LETS OUT A CHEER!**

On the ferry ride back to England, Jamison can't stop talking about the race and how he wants to be a race car driver someday. Then he pauses, thinking about the **WONDERFUL TIME HE HAD WITH HIS FATHER** at The Longest Day.

Jamison's father seems to be thinking the same thing. "Where to next, dad?" asked Jamison. "Home... we have some celebrating to do in Scotland," says his father.

"THEN PERHAPS ANOTHER RACE?"

EPILOGUE: JAGUAR IN THE '50'S - A DECADE OF DOMINANCE

The Ecurie Ecosse race team and driver Ron Flockhart would go on to prove that their amazing underdog victory in 1956 was not a fluke – they repeated their victory in 1957 in their iconic blue Jaguar D-Type. Not only that, but five out of the top six finishing positions in 1957 were held by Jaguar D-Types.

However, these two years were not the only wins for Jaguar in the 1950's. In fact, the marque was the most dominant manufacturer that decade.

Jaguar's success began with their C-Type racer which debuted with a Le Mans victory in 1951. It won again in 1953. The C-Type was a race version of the popular XK-120 road car (which is featured in The Longest Day as the green convertible driven by Jamison's father).

While the C-Type was a successful racer and the first to ever use disc brakes, it used a fairly basic tube-chassis layout. However, Jaguar completely reinvented how to build a racecar with the D-Type, which was first introduced in 1954.

The D-Type used methods proven in airplane construction to create a single chassis tub (called a "monocoque") with front and rear sections for the suspension, engine and other pieces.

The results speak for themselves – Jaguar D-Types won Le Mans three years in a row. The Jaguar Works team won in 1955, followed by the two Ecurie Ecosse victories. In total Jaguar racecars scored five Le Mans wins between 1950 and 1959. And, Jaguar scored many additional wins at top events like the 12 Hours of Sebring!

LE MANS VICTORIES IN THE 50'S
1951 | 1953 | 1955 | 1956 | 1957

WANT TO HAVE YOUR OWN RACE EXPERIENCE?

It is amazing that today parents can take their children to Le Mans or any other professional sports car race event around the world and have a similar adventure. Hopefully this book inspires you to go to a race, get up close to the cars and enjoy the sights and sounds of speed... and have a life-changing experience of your own!

WHAT'S NEXT FOR APEX LEGENDS?

There are exciting projects under development! Visit apexlegends.com and **SIGN-UP FOR THE NEWSLETTER** to receive the latest updates, product offers and more! Stay Connected:

f Apex Legends | The Longest Day

t @apex_legends | @longestdaybook

FEEDBACK IS WELCOME!

Did you enjoy sharing this book with your child or family member? Did this story remind you of the first time you were taken to a race?

Please email cworkman@apexlegends.com and share your thoughts on the book and your race memories!

This is where it all started – the first concept drawing for The Longest Day!

4

CPSIA information can be obtained at www.ICGtesting.com
Printed in the USA
BVOW07*0755221215

429177BV00004B/5/P